The Christmas Story

told by JANE WERNER
pictures by ELOISE WILKIN

simon and schuster · new york

THIS IS A BRAND-NEW BOOK, ILLUSTRATED ESPECIALLY FOR GOLDEN BOOKS

THE LITTLE GOLDEN BOOKS ARE PRODUCED UNDER THE SUPERVISION OF

MARY REED, Ph.D.

FORMERLY OF TEACHERS COLLEGE, COLUMBIA UNIVERSITY

Author and Artist

Jane Werner has written, edited, and compiled dozens of children's books under her own and pen names. She also plans and supervises the Golden Books from the Walt Disney Studio.

Eloise Wilkin has illustrated more than thirty children's books. Among the many Little Golden Books she has done are A DAY AT THE PLAYGROUND, HOLIDAYS, BUSY TIMMY, THE NEW BABY, and FIX IT, PLEASE.

This is mary, a girl of Galilee.

She lived long years ago, but such a wonderful thing happened to her that we remember and love her still.

One day an angel appeared to Mary.

"You are blessed among women," the angel said. "For you shall have a son, whom you shall name Jesus. He shall be called the Son of God, and his kingdom shall never end."

"I am glad to serve the Lord," said Mary. "May it be as you have said."

Then the angel left her.

Mary's heart was so filled with joy that she made up a song to sing.

"My soul doth praise the Lord," she sang. "And my spirit rejoices in God, my Saviour. For he has chosen me, his poor handmaiden. And from this day forward all generations shall call me blessed."

That was Mary's song.

ow in the village of Nazareth there lived a good man named Joseph, a carpenter by trade. He became Mary's husband, and he watched over her kindly as time passed.

When Joseph had to go from Nazareth up to Bethlehem in Judea, to pay his taxes in his father's town, Mary
went with him.

On the long, weary journey, Mary grew tired. They had to go slowly and pause often for her to rest.

When they reached Bethlehem at last, they found
many travelers there before them. The streets were full
of cheerful, jostling kinsmen.

The inns were crowded to the doors.
Though Joseph asked shelter only for his wife, every
innkeeper turned them away.

At last one innkeeper, seeing Mary's weariness and
need, showed them to a stable full of warm, sweet hay.

There Mary brought forth her son. And she wrapped him in swaddling clothes and laid him in the manger, since there was no room for them in the inn.

There were in that same country shepherds in the field, keeping watch over their flocks by night.

An angel of the Lord appeared to them in shining glory, and they were all afraid.

But the angel said to them:

"There is nothing to fear. I come to bring you news of a great joy which shall come to all people.

"For a child is born this day in Bethlehem — a Saviour who is Christ the Lord.

"And this shall be a sign to you. You shall find the babe wrapped in swaddling clothes and lying in a manger."

Suddenly the sky was full of angels, praising God and saying, "Glory to God in the highest, and on earth peace, good will toward men."

When the angels disappeared into heaven, the shepherds said to one another, "Let us go to Bethlehem and see this thing which the Lord has made known to us."

They hurried to the town and found Mary and
Joseph, and the babe lying in the manger.

When they had seen it, they told everyone they met what had been told them about this child. And everyone who heard it wondered at the things which were told them by the shepherds.

ow at the time when Jesus was a baby, some wise
men from the East came to Jerusalem.

"Where is he that is born King of the Jews?" they asked. "For we have seen his star in the East, and are come to worship him."

When Herod the King heard this, he was troubled in his wicked heart. He called the wise men to him and asked them just when the star had appeared.

Then he sent them off to Bethlehem, saying, "Go and search for the young child, and when you have found him, bring word back to me, that I may come and worship him also."

When they had heard the king, the wise men departed. Behold, the star which they had seen in the East went before them, till it stood over the place where Jesus lay.

When they saw the star, the wise men rejoiced and were glad. And when they came into the house, they saw the young child with Mary his mother, and bowed down and worshipped him.

They opened their treasures and laid before him gifts: gold and frankincense and myrrh.

Mary remembered these things and treasured them in her heart, while the child grew strong in spirit and full of wisdom. And the grace of God was upon him.